Dear *Daughter*

from you to me®

from you to me®

concept by
Neil & Peter Coxon

Dear *Daughter*

from you to me®

This book is for your Daughter's unique story.

It is for her to capture her life and experiences so far and develop her ideas and plans for the years to come.

Ask her to complete it carefully and, if she wants to, add some photographs or images to personalise it more.

When it is finished and shared with you, this will be a record of her life so far . . . a story that you will both treasure forever.

Dear

Here is a gift from me to you . . . for you to share with me.

It is for you to capture your thoughts and memories of your life so far and also consider your dreams and aspirations for the future.

There may be some questions that you prefer not to answer, so don't worry, just answer the ones you like.

When you are ready, I look forward to you sharing some or all of your answers with me. I would love to learn more about you and to help you achieve your dreams.

People say that we all have at least one book in us, and this will be one of yours.

The story of your life so far that we will treasure forever.

Thank you,

with love

What are some of your **earliest** memories?

What do you think people **thought of** you as a child?

What are some of the things you like doing in your life?

Tell me about some of the **best** things that have **happened** to you . . .

What have been some of your favourite holidays?

How would you **describe** yourself?

Who or what has been the biggest influence on you?

Who did you most admire or look up to when you were younger and why?

What was the first piece of music you bought?

What piece/s of music would you choose in your own favourite 'top 10' ?

What is the **naughtiest** thing you have ever done?

Tell me **something** about yourself that you

think no one else will **know** . . .

What are some of your favourite ways of spending a weekend?

Describe some of your fondest memories of the times we have spent together...

What are a few of your favourite things?

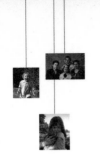

If you were an **animal** . . . what **type** of animal would you be, and why?

What do you think are your greatest strengths and weaknesses?

What have you found most difficult in your life?

With the benefit of hindsight, what would you do differently?

Describe some of the things you remember about your school days . . .

Tell me about some of your most **enjoyable** experiences at school . . .

What have you been best at during your time at school?

Describe your **favourite teachers** …
what is it about them you like and/or respect?

Thinking of your time at school, what do you think I am most proud of about you?

Tell me about your **best friends** ...

what do you **like** about them?

What do you enjoy doing with your friends?

How would you compare your male and female friends and how you get on with them?

What do you think your friends like most and least about you?

What do you like most about family life?

How well do you **get on with** the different people in our family?

What do you think I like most about you?

What do you think I **worry** about most with you?

What have you **most enjoyed** doing with our family . . . and **least** enjoyed?

What do I do that you appreciate and would like me to carry on doing?

What do I do that you do **not appreciate** and would like me to stop doing?

What do you like most, and least, about other members of our family?

Tell me about the family values you have learnt along the way that you would like to pass on . . .

What would you draw on from your childhood and upbringing when raising your own children?

This page is for you to write about other **members** of our family . . .

What advice would you like to give me or other members of our family?

What ideas have you had about what you wanted to do when you grew up and are things going to plan?

What sort of person did you think you would grow
to be and have you got there yet?

The future you . . .

Where would you like to travel to?

Where might you like to live and why?

Tell me about some of the things you would still like to do in your life . . .

What would you still love us to do together?

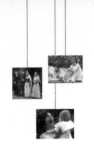

Are there any new things you would like to do with your friends?

If you won the Lottery . . . what would you do with the money?

If you could **travel** in **time** . . .

when and where would you go?

If you were granted three wishes...
what would they be and why?

Who do you most admire and why?

What is the best piece of advice you have been given . . . and how has it influenced you?

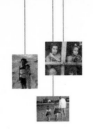

What **qualities** would you most like to be known for?

What would you like your **epitaph** to say?

Tell me about the dreams you have for your life . . .

Is there anything you would like to change about yourself or your life?

What would you like to do or have a go at in the next year?

Tell me about your **goals** and **aspirations** for
the next . . . 5 years / 10 years / 20 years

What can you do to **start achieving** your dreams and goals?

What can I do to help you achieve what you want?

And now your chance to write anything else
you want to say to me . . .

And finally for the record . . .

what is your full name ?

what is your date of birth ?

what colour are your eyes ?

how tall are you ?

what blood group are you ?

what was the date when you completed this story ?

Dear

Thank you for taking the time to complete this journal and I hope you would like to share some or all of it with me.

I hope you enjoyed answering my questions and developing your own plans. I would love to hear more about your memories as well as some of your dreams and I look forward to sharing more of your life in the future.

Thank you so much for doing it and for writing your own book . . .

from you to me

Dear Daughter

from you to me®

First published in the UK by *from you to me*, June 2009
Copyright, *from you to me* limited 2009
Hackless House, Murhill, Bath, BA2 7FH
www.fromyoutome.com
E-mail: hello@fromyoutome.com

ISBN 978-1-907048-07-4

Cover design by so design consultants, Wick, Bristol, UK
Printed and bound in the UK by CPI William Clowes, Beccles

This paper is manufactured from material sourced from forests certified according to strict environmental, social and economical standards.

If you think other questions should be included in future editions, please let us know. And please share some of the interesting answers you receive with us at the *from you to me* website to let other people read about these fascinating insights . . .

If you liked the concept of this book, please tell your family and friends and look out for others in the *from you to me* range:

Dear Mum, from you to me	*Dear Future Me, from you to me*
Dear Dad, from you to me	*Digging up Memories, from you to me*
Dear Grandma, from you to me	*Cooking up Memories, from you to me*
Dear Grandad, from you to me	*Kicking off Memories, from you to me*
Dear Sister, from you to me	*These were the days, from you to me*
Dear Brother, from you to me	*Christmas Present, Christmas Past, from you to me*
Dear Son, from you to me	other relationship and memory journals
Dear Friend, from you to me	available soon . . .